DISNEP

PLANES

pi kids
phoenix international publications, inc.

Dusty Crophopper has always dreamed of racing in the Wings Around The Globe Rally. As he gets ready for the qualifying race, he sees the superstar Ripslinger. Can you find this Ripslinger fan gear?

Ripslinger toy

Green Tornado lunch box

Green Tornado decal

Ripslinger cap

Team RPX flag

Ripslinger mug

Dusty qualified for the race! Skipper offered to help him train. Look around Propwash Junction for Skipper and these other locals who will be rooting for Dusty:

Sparky

Skipper

Mayday

Chug

Leadbottom

Dottie

Franz is one of only six German cars that can transform into an airplane. Can you find Franz and the five others like him in the oil-hall?

While flying above the Taj Mahal, Dusty realizes he's a long way from home. See if you can find these things that make him homesick:

Skipper's star insignia

tractor

American tourist

can of ethanol

Vita-minamulch sign

Chug look-alike

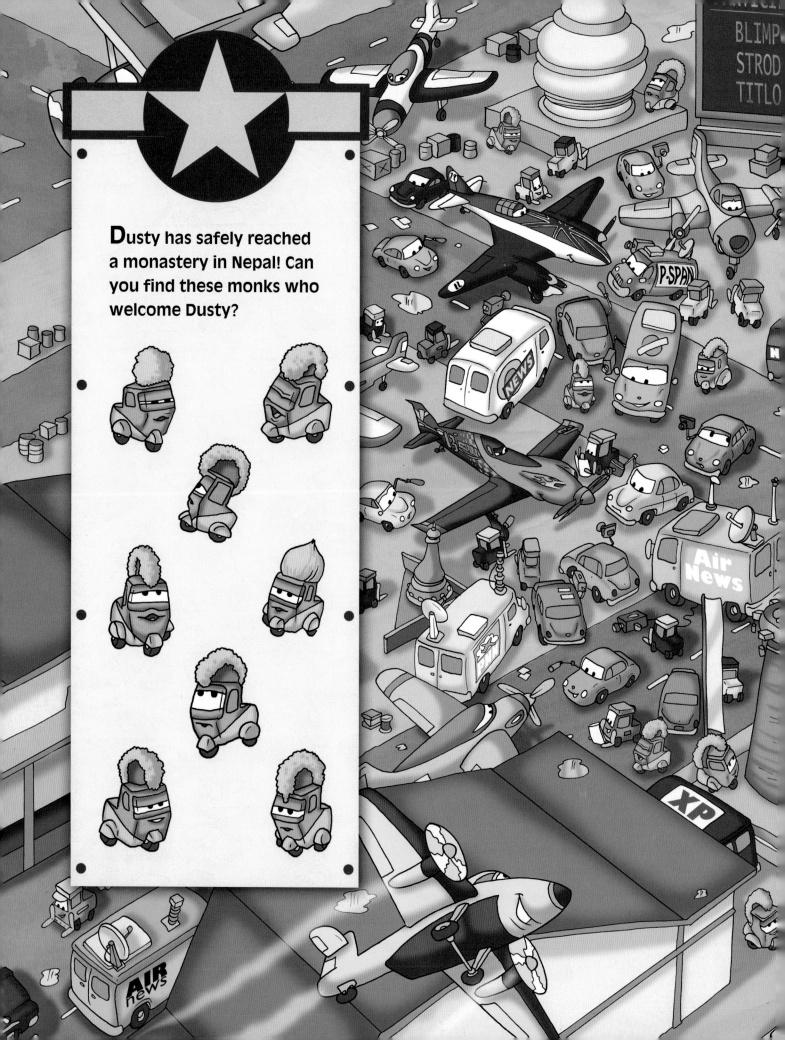

Dusty has safely reached a monastery in Nepal! Can you find these monks who welcome Dusty?

The Jolly Wrenches are giving Dusty some help! See if you can find these members of Skipper's former navy squadron:

this shooter tug

this yellow gear tug

this navy tug

Bravo

this fighter

Captain

Echo

As Dusty gets ready for the final leg of the race, he needs to get fixed up. Will you find these plane parts that can replace his broken ones?

propeller

GPS

speed pump

hydraulic pump

flow control valve

starter generator

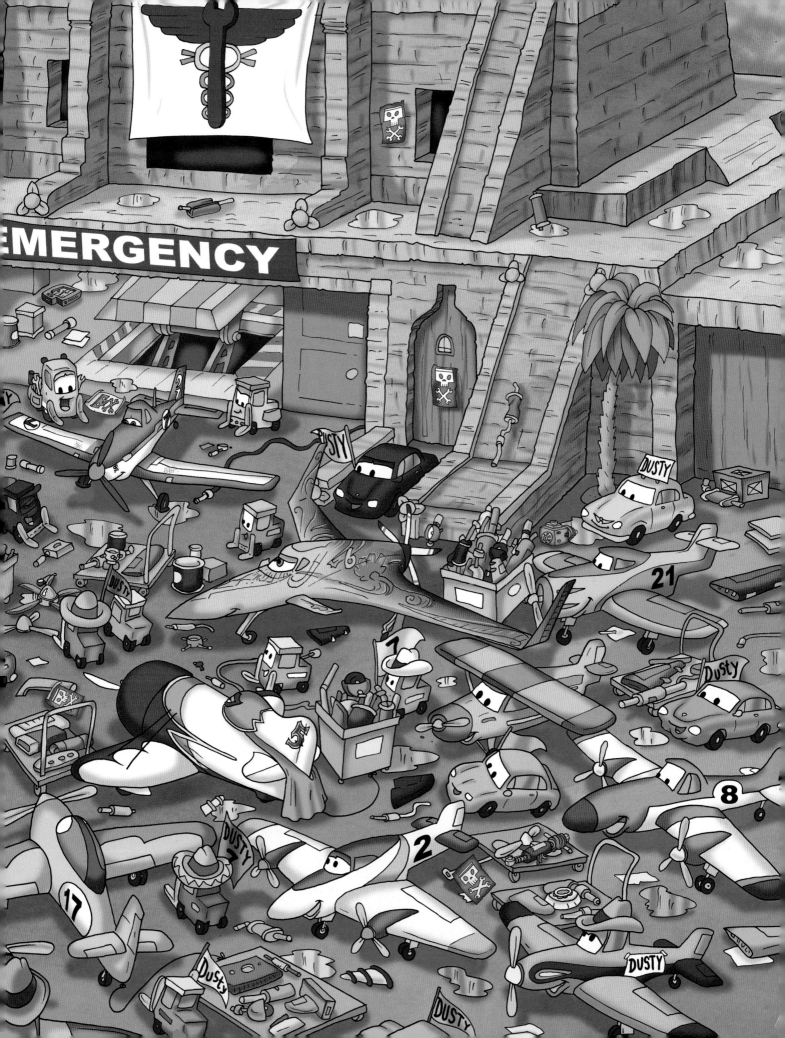

Dusty has won the Wings Around The Globe Rally! Can you find his fans' favorite memorabilia?

Dusty toy

Crophopper flag

Dusty whistle

Dusty bobblehead

I'll Keep FLYING LOW poster

Dusty foam wings

Dusty hat

Dusty lunch box

Ned and Zed are twin planes known as the Twin Turbos! Fly back to the qualifying race and see if you can find them and these other pairs of twins:

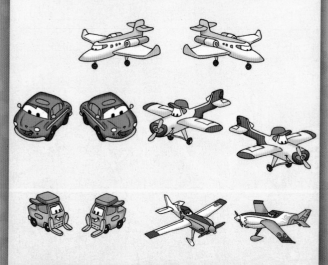

Propwash Junction is a great place to live and work. Head back to town and find these products that are made there:

can of ethanol

bottle of corn oil

bag of cornstarch

tire

spark plug

windshield washer fluid

After a tough race, Dusty and El Chupacabra go to a German oil-hall. Can you find these flags from countries included in the Wings Around The Globe Rally?

Iceland

Germany

China

India

Mexico

USA

While Ishani shows Dusty around India, the two planes become friends. Look on all the planes at the Taj Mahal to find these letters that spell "Ishani":

Dusty is quickly becoming a new star in the racing world. Every major news channel across the globe is covering him! Try to find the logos of these top networks:

The Jolly Wrenches keep a Wall of Fame that shows every mission for every flyer. Go back and look for these plaques and medals from previous missions:

Dusty wouldn't have made it to Mexico without the help of the Jolly Wrenches. Can you find these symbols of the Jolly Wrenches in Mexico?

Chug and Sparky run Dusty's fan club. Every member gets a Dusty Fan Club sticker. Go back to the finish line and try to find 24 stickers.

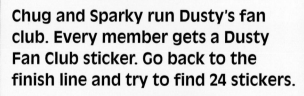